HEALING
IN THE
POTTER'S HOUSE

Lizzie Hunt

O&U
Onwards & Upwards

Onwards and Upwards Publishers

4 The Old Smithy, London Road, Rockbeare,
EX5 2EA, United Kingdom.

www.onwardsandupwards.org

First edition, published in the United Kingdom by Onwards and Upwards Publishers Ltd. (2024).

ISBN:	978-1-78815-787-2
Typeface:	Sabon LT

This is a work of fiction. Names, characters, businesses, places, events, locales, and incidents are either the products of the author's imagination or used in a fictitious manner. Any resemblance to actual persons, living or dead, or actual events is purely coincidental.

Scripture quotations are from or similar to The Authorized (King James) Version. Rights in the Authorized Version in the United Kingdom are vested in the Crown. Reproduced by permission of the Crown's patentee, Cambridge University Press.

Endorsements

Take a walk with Lizzie and the Lord as He ministers truth and grace to the woundedness she feels after the death of her husband, Garry. It is breathtaking to experience God healing Lizzie's heart. You will be caught away in this living encounter with the Living God, and sense Him ministering directly to your heart as you read.

Dr Mark Virkler
Founder, Communion with God Ministries

I recommend that you read this book out loud! My first read was a cursory one, as Lizzie had invited my reflections. Initially, I was rather inattentive, as I was reading while endeavouring to form a valued opinion. However, as a friend and I began to read it out loud together, we both became overwhelmed when our emotions interrupted us. We felt Lizzie's heart stream from every page as her eloquent poetic words painted a picture. This book excels in illustrating what it means to be loved, healed and restored. It impacted and gripped us and we couldn't put it down. A must-read.

Reverend Giles Cornell MA
Pastor, Lighthouse Church, Ely

When I first read this book, I had questions. I wondered if it was born out of Lizzie's real experience or whether it was what you might call 'sanctified imagination'. Or did it just touch me because I knew Lizzie and Garry personally? Whatever the origins, I have wept every time I have read it, and I've come to the conclusion that it is the Holy Spirit who touches me as I read it .

Essentially, this book illustrates a journey – a journey in which the Potter and the Holy Spirit and Jesus take Lizzie through the pain of losing her beloved husband.

For me, it is a journey that is more than imagination; it has true spiritual reality. Each room she visits in the Potter's House has an impact on her, and she responds remarkably honestly in each situation. Also, Jesus feels so extraordinarily real to me as she meets with Him!

I have no doubt that the Holy Spirit had a hand in this writing and it will bless many people, and there are many ideas and phrases in it that I will never forget.

Margaret Cornell
Pastor and author

Lizzie leads us into the dimension where "heaven is as real as earth". I feel soothed and comforted, healed and restored as I read *Healing in the Potter's House*. Lizzie is an authentic messenger with a living relationship with God – born of a consistency of fellowship with Him that I have witnessed across many years. This book is birthed by the Spirit; enjoy its riches!

Rebecca Duckworth MA,
'Hearing God's Voice' UK team

Contents

Contents Continued

Foreword by L. MacAlpine

After the death of her husband, Lizzie needed to take stock of her life. Where was she in her process of grief? Was she grieving 'normally' or not? Had she received any answers to her many questions, she who had believed he would recover after so much prayer? Should she be ashamed of having believed? And how was she to deal with the reality of the pain of emptiness and silence left by Garry? And what about God... Where was He? Could she ever trust herself – or Him – to rebuild the close relationship she had enjoyed since childhood?

Encouraged by friends, Lizzie started to write, without knowing where it would take her. Her book engages us in a dialogue between her and the Potter, with the ever-present help of her friend the Holy Spirit. The book is full of gentleness, movement and light, rooms to visit, doors to open and much more. The 'Mirrors of Time' give her the opportunity to reinterpret her life. It's a metaphorical and sensory journey all the way to heaven (and back). On her journey, Lizzie discovers that the pieces of her formerly well-controlled but now shattered life have been carefully set aside by the Potter to be reassembled into a priceless vase. She also discovers a celestial railway junction where she can give herself permission to leave everything behind that she wishes to – or dares to – and risk taking a fresh route. She finds herself able and ready to continue living without the husband she loved, and with neither shame nor regret, but with a new and living hope.

For me, her book is about the subtle but powerful way in which the mysterious Potter and her Friend the Holy Spirit accompany her through the grieving process.

L. MacAlpine
Youth with a Mission

Introduction

Have you ever, deep down in the depths of wherever your heart of hearts is, cherished a flickering pilot light of hope that heaven is in the here and now, that it might be possible to communicate with wherever God's heart of hearts is? You know, talk to Him as though He were in your home with you, or maybe you in His home with Him? I believe we can, and this book chronicles my expedition into a world where heaven is as real as earth, but somehow safer and more permanent; where everything is ordered in all things and secure, where faith receives her answers and where evil is forbidden. My hope is that this tour through the Potter's house will serve as a match to that pilot-light hope and ignite in you the same passion that I have, to hear from God every day about – well – every day.

It's not as though I have ever doubted the existence of God and heaven. I can't begin to guess at how young I was when I asked Jesus to come into my life through the door in my heart, which I could visualise perfectly (just as I could visualise tiny people walking in and out of a door into our black-and-white TV). Throughout my early years and teens, I prayed as though God were listening and learned my Bible as though it were true. This became much more real, I would say, when I encountered the baptism in the Holy Spirit in my college years and my Christianity became what I had hoped it could be: closer, deeper, more alive. However – and what a 'however' this was – it was still somewhat one-sided. I would write pages and pages of my own thoughts and prayers to God, including what I thought He might be saying if only He would talk to me – but was it real?

The answers began to unfold when I attended a sweet Pentecostal church in my hometown, where we experienced something of a revival, with many young people converted and the gifts of the Spirit exercised freely. I enjoyed giving and receiving Bible-based prophetic words under the steady eye of our dynamic young pastor. When a new young man joined the church, I laid out what we called a 'fleece' for guidance about whether we should marry. (The fleece method is found in the story of Gideon in the Bible and involves asking God to do a certain thing to demonstrate His will. I do not recommend it.) The fleece 'worked' and we married, became leaders in the church and had two wonderful children. Unfortunately, the marriage itself did not 'work' and I was left wondering again if there wasn't something more substantial in this relationship with God. I'm sorry to say that I took the lazy way out and gave up on it all, challenging God with, "If this is real, You'll have to make it real to me!" Life and spiritual confusion went from bad to worse until – oh, happy day – I heard a couple of Christian songs at a toddler's party. The lady who sang may never know this, but her songs reignited that pilot light deep down in the depths of wherever my heart of hearts is. I knew I had given up on the most real thing ever, so I went straight to the back of the local church, fell to my knees and cried, "If You can do anything with this mess of my life, You can have it."

I would like to say that a shining angel appeared, struck me on the shoulder with the bracing words, "Rise, you mighty woman of valour!" – but no. I walked home and resumed Christian disciplines and fellowship, ineffably grateful for total forgiveness and restoration through the Cross. The springtime freshness of renewed relationship with God sustained me through the desolation of the break-up of my marriage. Unfortunately, though, I became aware again of that desperate longing for deep closeness with God. I would kneel before my Bible on my fireside chair, grab and punch the cushion, calling out, "Speak to me! I must hear Your voice!" And that was enough for a loving Father who wants nothing more than this sort of intimacy. Two things happened.

Firstly, I came across a book[1] about biblical meditation by someone called Campbell McAlpine. I had no idea who he was, but the content of the book was like an oasis in my desert. I drank thirstily, following his guidelines to the letter, until I genuinely felt that I was safely receiving inspiration from the Holy Spirit in the solid ground of Scripture. The springtime freshness was producing blossom!

It was at this juncture that I made contact with the church I now attend and which I love as family. I say "I made contact" but in actual fact, they reached out to me and supported me and the children through it all. I had been ashamed to reveal the extent of my backsliding to old friends, but they treated me as the forgiven and restored child of God that I was, and I am eternally grateful to them. I hope I will always treat others with that innocent acceptance.

Here, in this church, I have been nurtured, healed and understood by family and friends and by my loving heavenly Father. Here, I met and married, loved and served with my

---

[1] *The Practice of Biblical Meditation*

Garry. And here, still surrounded by family and friends, I said goodbye to him. So I would like to thank my precious son and daughter and their families, the Lighthouse Church and many, many other friends for travelling with me to the point where I can write this book as a reflection of all that matters most to me in my Christian life.

1

I Meet the Potter

So, at the door the Potter asked, "What brought you here?"

"I was lonely," I replied. "My husband Garry died. I have so many questions and a completely blank horizon and an unfamiliar context, being alone for the first time in so many years, and a widow of all things." I knew I was gabbling, so I slowed down and said, "I just thought about a retreat, and while I was there, I found this place."

"Tell me more," the Potter said.

"After he died, so unexpectedly, there was so much to do, even in the fog of grief. My children gathered round me, as stunned as me. People were so kind; it was almost overwhelming. I could hardly take a breath, but family and friends and my precious church were there to lift and help. I would never have made it through those first steps of widowhood without their love and support. Then my daughter and her family had to go back to Asia, and my son and his wife had to stay away because of Covid, and I was alone, silent. If I didn't make a noise, there was no noise; if I didn't do something, nothing happened. No music, no doors opening, no car crunching up the drive, no comments, no jokes. Nothing. But somehow, in the vast and cold mist, I knew that the next step through this uncharted vacuum was to visit my sister on the coast."

"What happened there?" he asked, with no small talk, no preamble. He was persuasive and yet so undemanding.

"Well, I took a walk along the beach and my Friend the Holy Spirit reassured me that this journey could continue to be taken gently, one step at a time. The next step was the retreat."

"You were brave to come," he acknowledged with a smile.

I thought, *you know it.* But I said, "I was more nervous about the drive down. My husband would drive me around in his classic Jaguar, and I'm borrowing a little Honda Jazz!"

"You planned the route very carefully," he commented.

I wondered how he knew that this had been a major hurdle in the venture, but I said, "Oh yes! I wrote it down and memorised it step by step because I like to know where I'm going and I don't trust my mobile phone or my own navigational skills."

"That was a joke between Garry and you," the Potter chuckled. Again, I was surprised – and comforted – first that he knew and then that he would talk to me about these sensitive subjects.

I replied, "Yes, it was." Then I paused for a few moments, reflecting on this joke, another treasure from our marriage, and wondering what I would ever do with it.

"What was your main emotion on the way down?" the Potter asked after the kindest moment.

"Well, once I was in the car, I became progressively more relieved. I'd done it! I had planned and prepared and organised this step by myself! The house was secure and the car was running well. I prayed and worshipped all the way, actually! I felt so grateful to everyone who had helped and encouraged me, and most of all to my Friend the Holy Spirit in the car with me."

"I think you feel peaceful now," he observed.

"Once I knew the programme for this retreat, I felt peace," I admitted. "I don't like not knowing what's happening or what will happen next."

"During your walk on the beach, what did the Holy Spirit say about your future?"

"Nothing!" I replied, vehemently. "He seemed to say only that the next step would become evident as I took this one."

The Potter paused again. I felt he was looking straight through me.

"There is another reason you chose to come here..." It was spoken as a matter of fact.

"I don't want to talk about that yet," I dared to say.

"Quite right," he agreed, to my relief. "That is not a threshold conversation. There are many rooms in this house and I will take you through them. You can ask what you like when you feel ready, even in the grief room. Sometimes you will go in alone with your Friend the Holy Spirit, and you can tell me what He said – if you choose to. All your years of daily waiting at our doors[2] has prepared you for this. Be sure that not one journal entry was wasted. Each was its own investment."

---

[2]   Proverbs 8:34

I was elated! Every inch of space I had emptied to listen to my Friend mattered! All those times I had been discouraged because I had thought I was following a mind-map around my own head or writing to the floor underneath my desk! As I pondered this with gratitude, I looked down and saw the mosaic flooring in the entrance hall.

"Yes," the Potter said, following my gaze. His eyes were glistening. "Every word is heard and read and sifted and reconstituted until we have the perfect combination for your path of life, footprints and all. This is where your treasured memories will be placed." I was so happy that he had understood my earlier thoughts; I wouldn't always have to try to explain my cacophony of emotions in this house.

It was then that I remembered the muddy boots I had spotted outside the door and the disturbing effect they had had on me.

2

About the Boots

I had a question about those boots, a fuzzy memory from a dream, but I hesitated from embarrassment.

"Now," the Potter said, "you're fretting about those boots in your dream."

"Yes," I confessed in wonder, again glad that he had introduced a sensitive topic; such a relief that I didn't have to mention or justify my feelings.

"I know how they got muddy," I admitted.

"Go on," he urged.

It was easy to confess, much easier than not confessing! It always is, I suppose.

"They were miles too big for me, but in my dream I was determined to wear those boots on this path of grief and mourning, thinking they would protect me from the miry clay."[3]

The Potter's compassionate expression invited me to continue.

"I got stuck of course," I shrugged.

---

[3]   Psalm 40:2

"...and your strong Prince came to rescue you!" He clapped his hands in triumph.

"I didn't want to be rescued. Those boots represented my unanswered questions, my challenges, my consternation, the desolation of my failed prayers. I had a right to wear those boots, I told myself in my confusion."

"And then your Prince of Peace offered to lift you out of your confusion, out of the miry clay, and to set your feet on a rock and establish your goings!"[4] He was singing now, so I continued the tale.

"He didn't give up, you know, and my Friend the Holy Spirit made me realise that the most logical of all my options was to follow His advice!"

The Potter paused again before he replied, evidently giving me time to consider that my Friend often does that when I'm struggling to do His will. Eventually, he said, "And now you're wondering how the boots came to stand outside this house, still caked in mud?"

"My Friend advised me not to go back for them, you see."

"Of course! You were wearing socks! And the boots were too big for you anyway. But your Prince brought them along because one day – perhaps – they won't be too big."

Somehow this cryptic comment was enough for me. And somehow in this special place my questions were quieted because I knew that there were answers. It was just that I didn't know them yet.

---

[4] Psalm 40:2

"Hold that thought!" the Potter interrupted. "The answers are known, but not yet by you; this will bring you security and peace."

The relief of knowing that these were not random unanswerable mysteries was tremendous. The mosaic seemed orderly and smooth, just how I like things, until I noticed jagged black stones placed irregularly in the pattern.

3

My First Encounter with the Mirrors of Time

To my horror, a violent geyser of passionate fury burst from me!

"No," I exploded, "it cannot be random! I cannot accept that the path of my life is a random array of things I've said and done. You said you had sifted them. Why are these broken black ones spoiling the pattern?"

The Potter's hand was on my shoulder as he let me finish. We were both weeping. Then he led me – oh, so gently – to a mirror on the far wall. Rubbing my tears with my white knuckles, I looked and saw the reflection of the floor. To my surprise there were words! From this angle, all those random black spots were letters!

I had to focus for a while and then I read, "What I am doing, you don't understand now, but you will know hereafter."[5]

I was astonished! "How does it do that?" I asked. "I can't make out the words without the mirror!"

---

[5] John 13:7

The Potter gave a knowing smile, almost smug. I could tell he had been longing to give me this revelation.

"This is called a Mirror of Time'," he explained. "You will find them throughout the house. Years ago you wrote, 'Will mirrors of time show what now seems to be?'"

"I remember," I said. "I wrote that poem after my divorce:

> *What will I remember, twenty years on*
> *When I reflect on the things that are gone,*
> *Will I look then through the lens I now see,*
> *Will mirrors of time show what now seems to be?*"

"One day," the Potter assured me, "the Mirrors of Time will tell you the truth about your whole life."

"One day," I sighed, "when the boots fit!"

"When the boots fit," he agreed, "but not now."

Then he giggled.

"What's funny?" I asked.

"'Now' is such a funny word in heaven. I mean, *really* funny." He could hardly contain himself. "Because there isn't any other!"

He paused, searching my face for the light to dawn. It didn't.

Now he was sighing! "We'll put that one in the boots," he laughed, and led me on with an indulgent pat on my shoulder. It was then that I noticed the curtain.

4

The Eucharist Room

"This room is for you to go into alone," the Potter urged. The curtain opened as I stepped forward. It was so thick and heavy, yet it had opened by itself just for me![6] As soon as I entered, my whole being was assailed by sensations stronger than I'd ever known. I smelt freshly baked bread, I saw a golden chalice of sparkling wine, I heard angels singing, my feet touched the carpet of... of... *holy ground*, and there was the sweetest taste in my mouth.

There at the table I sensed the Presence of my Prince of Peace. "Welcome!" He said heartily. "Come, eat and drink and let us be merry, for yesterday I died."

Well, this was new!

I didn't know what to do or say. Of course, He knew, like the Potter knew, like my Friend always knows.

"You're wondering whether we shouldn't be solemn at this Eucharistic feast," He observed. "There is indeed a time and a place for such solemnity. But today is a day to celebrate. Let's celebrate *you*!"

I was bewildered, upside down!

---

[6] Luke 23:45

"I thought I was supposed to celebrate You?"

"Of course, always; but here in my Presence, remember also that you are the joy that was set before Me, so that I could endure the cross, despising the shame.[7] You are one I brought to glory when I was being made the perfect captain of your salvation through suffering!"[8] He was singing now! Rejoicing over me with singing![9]

"Oh, come now," He said, catching my expression, "don't let's countenance the impostor syndrome! There is nothing unworthy about being one I died for, because there is nothing worthy about it!"

He went on to talk for hours – or was it seconds? – about His joys and triumphs and the treasures of my salvation. I marvelled. I had come here with nothing, the curtain had opened by itself, and I was feasting with the King of Kings! I looked around this fragrant room, for a second taking my eyes off His compelling Presence. It was then that I noticed the windows.

---

[7] Hebrews 12:2
[8] Hebrews 2:10
[9] Zephaniah 3:17

5

In the Presence of My Enemies

At the windows all around the room (except for one wall which seemed to be a fire of burning incense), I saw the most grotesque images of my worst fears, doubts and failures. They were mocking, sneering, accusing, leering, laughing. I hadn't noticed them while I was absorbed in His Presence and celebrating the joys of salvation, but now...

My Prince of Peace had noticed my distraction, of course, and I asked Him, "How can they be here?"

"Oh, them!" He said in derision. "They are always with you in your earthly walk, but have I not prepared this table before you in the presence of your enemies?[10] No evil can come near you here. Go and see for yourself. Go to the window."

"Will You come with me?" I pleaded.

"If they see Me with you, they will scatter in terror," He said, "but go on; fear no evil for I am with you."[11]

I inched my way towards the window. The enemies redoubled their efforts to terrify me, mouthing ugly accu-

---

[10] Psalm 23:5
[11] Psalm 23:4

sations, until... a forcefield! I sprang back in amazement, and they slunk away in defeat. I looked back at my Prince, questioning.

"Do you see?" He laughed. "You are in the secret place of the Most High!"[12]

We laughed and celebrated some more, but then He was serious. "Whenever you eat this bread and drink this cup, remember," He said earnestly. "Remember[13] to celebrate what I have done (you can be solemn then, sometimes you will weep for My love); and celebrate the benefits of Calvary (you can dance then if you like, you are allowed). And that's another reason to leave those heavy boots at the door!" He added in a whisper, smiling now.

"Remember, too, the victories, the defeated foes, and carry those images to the earthly table. Your Friend will help you. He will always help you. He loves to help you."[14]

I thought this was my cue to leave, but it was then that I noticed the urn.

---

[12] Psalm 91:1
[13] 1 Corinthians 11:25
[14] John 14:26

6

About the Urn

On the table with the bread and wine (and actually some other dishes, but those were for another time, I knew) there was an urn, an urn for ashes. Strangely, it was bubbling, rattling; surely the lid could not stay on much longer! The Prince of Peace looked delightedly at the pot.

"Yes," He exclaimed, "some of them are ready!"

He looked at me and held out His hand, nail-pierced of course. Again, I didn't dare to assume what to do, but it didn't matter. He beckoned me. *Me!* He hugged me with those nail-pierced hands and held me to His wounded side, and I knew it was for me He had died. That moment was more important than anything in the world to me – the sparkling wine, the fresh bread, the enemies at the window (looking ragged now), the fascinating force-field, the strange self-opening curtain, the bubbling pot – all those vivid impressions were absorbed into one consuming hug. I thought my heart would break with satisfaction.

Eventually He said, "Well, I must deal with these bubbling ans— but no! I'll let the Potter tell you about it. Go now." He gestured to the bread and wine. "Remember Me."

I trembled through the open curtain and stood silent on my mosaic. It was shining now with gold I hadn't noticed before.

"Would you tell me about it?" the Potter asked tentatively.

So I did.

"Can I ask you, did you see a pot?"

"The urn?" I queried. "Yes, I did."

"And was it... bubbling, nearly bursting?"

"It was," I said and started when he leapt back.

"Oh glory, glory, glory, glory, glory, glory!" he chanted. "And more and more glory!" He paused and looked at me until he understood. "He didn't tell you what they were?" he guessed.

"He said you could tell me," I answered.

"Oh, He is so kind! He knows I love this one."

I was intrigued. "What makes the pot bubble?"

"The pot bubbles when some answers to prayer are ready."

I was excited now, but first I had a question.

"What is the meaning of the urn? Surely this symbolises death!"

"The requests have to die with Him first, of course; many dreams and visions have died in that urn, but in due time you receive freshly boiled answers if you don't faint on the way.[15] And then the Father is glorified in the Son!"[16] he finished triumphantly. Of course, that set him off on his glory chant again, and this time I joined in because at that moment I

---

[15] Galatians 6:9
[16] John 14:13

couldn't think of anything more wonderful than the Father being glorified in the Son. Somehow it didn't matter what answers were in that urn so long as all of heaven was glorified. *How different from my earthly take on answered prayer,* I mused to myself.

"Yes," he agreed (I was sure I had not spoken aloud), "on earth, where the most important thing is to get what you want."

"And then we contort the process to give it some sort of glory spin!" I could see that clearly now, and recognised this as a Mirror of Time correcting a memory.

I couldn't resist my next comment though, so, trying not to sound petulant, I blurted out, "I thought I was promised that the end of Garry's sickness would be glory. I so wanted him healed and I thought it would be resurrection glory *in this life.* Where is the glory in his pain and death?" I was ranting now, chin up, eyes blazing. My questions hung in the air like piercing arrows of sound, tearing apart my fragile mask of resignation.

"My dear, dear child," he said, "My dear, dear, precious child. There, there… shh, shh."

I was comforted. I was honestly, down to the soul, comforted. He soothed me till I lowered my defiant chin, melted.

It was then that I noticed the broken pottery on the floor by a door.

7

Pottery Rooms

"Oh no!" I cried with my hands covering my face. "Did I do that when I was ranting?"

"This has to stop, Lizzie!"

I looked up, startled, for his voice sounded stronger than I'd heard him before. This was important. "There is no glory or credit in taking responsibility for every crisis and event. You are not the centre of the world." Then he winked. And then I laughed. I laughed at myself! A liberating laugh for all those self-important sighs, self-deprecating shrugs and self-accusing gasps.

The Potter laughed too, until he cried, sad now. "Remember the bread and the wine. Let Him be the centre of your world, the King enthroned, the all-sufficient One you refer to before you misdirect attention to yourself." I was chastened, but in a 'let's move forward, we can do this together' sort of way. He opened the door and urged me on with his staff. This was so kind of him, because otherwise I would have drifted into self-condemnation, and he knew it.

There were broken pots everywhere, and I noticed they were being sorted into piles very, very carefully.

"What's happening here?" I asked.

"Look at the doors," the Potter said. Several doors led off this room, each with a label. The first read "The Right Amount of Time".

"The right amount of time until the mended pot is toughened?" I stabbed. I know very little about pottery.

"Oh no," the Potter chuckled, "the right amount of time before the pot is mended. We leave it until the owner forgets its original detail so that we can return it to his current reality."

I was mystified and stayed silent for once. He went on to explain.

"So often you have wanted us to replicate immediately what has been broken or lost in your life, returning the pot as it was then; but if we did that, you'd want everything – and everyone – in your life to recreate its context. So, we give it back in a shape and pattern and strength that fits your life as it is now, your current reality, correcting the memories in the Mirrors of Time."

This was just making sense even to my impatient tendencies. However, I had a question. "Surely, if you gave it back straight away, my life would not have moved on, so it would still be my current reality?"

"True," he agreed, "but only we know what happens next and the good plans we have for you, the future and the hope.[17] We know exactly when the bowl will need to contain what it is designed for. Pots don't grow on trees, you know. In fact, they don't grow at all." We shared a grin; I was so glad he understood my sense of humour.

---

[17] Jeremiah 29:11

"Relationships are the speciality in this room," he commented.

Oh.

The Potter had pulled the plug on my amusement. I knew he meant that the broken pieces of relationships could not be repaired in a hurry, and I so wanted the ups and downs of my marriage to be transformed quickly into healthy memories.

"Yes, each must move forward at his own pace until the bowl of his story is ready to be returned. Truth must stand at the whipping-post."

I didn't understand, so he continued.

"There is always a way forward, the way of truth, but each must beat the truth until they find it to be unshakable, a foundation for a new beginning. Once you know the truth (and your Friend will always tell you the truth)[18], the truth in the Mirrors of Time will set you free."[19]

I began to see that there is no need for angry self-justification or tweaking of the facts when there is an objective truth.

"No," he said, "the truth will fight for itself, if you will admit it to yourself."

I found this hard to accept and I looked away, silent, the Potter giving time for the truth to do its work in me. It was then that I saw the golden door – pure gold, I was sure.

---

[18] John 16:13
[19] John 8:32

8

Kintsugi

The label on the door was "Kintsugi". I had no idea what that meant, but I was sure by now that all would become clear, so I followed the Potter into the room.

"This is an art form you will see on earth," the Potter explained. "The broken pots are repaired with gold, so that what was meant for evil turns out better than the original.[20] It embraces imperfections."

The effect was stunning. All around the room there were magnificent specimens of exquisitely recreated vessels. The seams were glorious, celebrated rather than disguised. Here, I mused, you could glory in your weaknesses.[21]

"Let me show you", he beckoned and took some dirty, broken pieces in his hand. He lifted them to his face and looked and looked until he cried. He cried for all the pain that had broken that pot, and he washed it with his tears. Then he breathed words of love and healing until it was dry.

"How can you see what it was like?" I asked in awe.

---

[20] Genesis 50:20
[21] 2 Corinthians 12:9

"We don't see for long what it was like," he smiled, "but we do see what it is like now, and we can see what it will be." He gave me a sweet smile, reassuring me that one day I would understand this 'now' business. Then, with anticipatory concentration, he applied the gold generously, lavishly, meticulously, until he had created a thing of exquisite delicacy, almost transparent, and yet... "Watch this," he said and dropped it on the floor! It rolled to my feet, and picking it up in wonder, I returned it to him reverently.

"Oh no," he said. "It is yours, one of your life answers from the bubbling urn."

As I examined this translucent treasure, I was astounded to discover that it contained something like liquid mother-of-pearl, liquid that had not been spilt in all the bowl's adventures.

I had to ask.

"What is this liquid?"

"This is your husband's love for you," the Potter said tenderly. "The reality of his love was not lost when he left you to be with us, when your heart was pierced by the grief of his bodily suffering. Carry it as a precious possession. Your Friend the Holy Spirit will help you. Never forget the privilege of being loved as you were; so many hearts have ached for such love. It will not spill as we move on."

I was weeping copiously by now, and as my tears fell into the bowl, the most glorious fragrance was released, the purest scents of the forests my Garry loved.

"Every time you cry," the Potter said, "remember this fragrance. You have been loved. You have been loved."

He waited patiently as I reflected on this most wonderful of gifts, until eventually I looked up from the shimmering bowl.

It was then that I noticed the note pinned to the next door.

9

Treasures of Darkness

It was addressed to me, and the Potter motioned for me to open it. The script was somehow familiar and read like my everyday journalling...

Dear Lizzie,

Remember we were talking about Jeremiah going to the Potter's house? You memorised chapter 18, verse 2:

"Arise and go down to the Potter's house, and there I will cause you to hear my words."

You so want to hear my words and I love you for it, and here you are! This next room contains treasures of darkness.[22] Don't be afraid of the dark in there for I am with you, even as I have been with you through this valley of the shadow of death,[23] even as I have been with you throughout your life since

---

[22] Isaiah 45:3
[23] Psalm 23:4

(and even before) you invited Me to live within your heart as a tiny child.

So come with Me, your Friend, and let us run together![24]

I ran. I was not afraid!

The Potter called after me, "Let me give you a tip! Remember the Bible verses you have learnt!"

Immediately the door flew open and I found myself on a sort of travelator in the dark, the pitch dark. The door slammed behind me. I didn't know where I was or what to do, but I heard the sweet voice of my Friend saying, "Remember the Potter's advice."

I cast around in my memory for a verse that would apply in darkness until, at last, up came, "Your word is a lamp to my feet and a light for my path."[25]

Immediately as I said it aloud, tiny tea-lights appeared just in front of me and something like miners' lamps lit up on my toes. But now the noises started, like the ghost-trains of my childhood fairground forays; voices too, the old enemies from the windows in the Eucharist room, mocking, screaming. I felt as though I was being pelted with small rocks which clung to my clothes. As I tried in vain to brush them off, I fell and could not rise from sitting. I knew my Friend was with me, so why wasn't He doing something? I was in the dark, on the travelator, being transported who knows where, taunted and attacked by the enemies, and I couldn't hear His voice.

---

[24] Song of Songs 1:4
[25] Psalm 119:105

A thought hit me: *Act on the last thing He said to you. What was the last thing He said to me? Ah yes, the Potter's advice. Any verses about enemies or devils? Think, Lizzie, think! Help me, my Friend!*

A word: "Resist..."

Oh yes, "Resist the devil and he will flee."[26] *But how? How to resist?*

A whisper: "How did your Prince resist in the wilderness?"

In the wilderness, in the wilderness – yes! "It is written..." [27]

A sword appeared in my hand[28] and I brandished it wildly.

But what? What is written?

Another prompt: "The Name..."

Of course! "The Name above every name!"[29]

I was shouting the Name now, strengthened on the inside, lunging purposefully with the sword. "Every knee shall bow at the Name, every tongue confess He is Lord!"

Immediately, there was a clatter as though everything in the room was dropping, plopping, flopping down; the voices were silent except for a few begrudging whimpers, "We know, we know." Others hissed, "She knows too. We have to flee." And they did.

---

[26] James 4:7b
[27] Ephesians 6:17
[28] Matthew 4:1-11
[29] Philippians 2:9

An eerie silence. The travelator was still moving, I was still sitting, but I was safe, I knew. A song from years and years ago started singing itself in my head and my heart:

"Rejoice not against me, O mine enemy:
When I fall, I shall arise;
When I sit in darkness,
The LORD shall be a light unto me."[30]

Immediately as I sang, the door ahead of me flew open and light burst in. The Potter was there to lift me to my feet. Blinking at the bright light, and dizzy with relief, I heard a musical tinkling sound. There at my feet were jewels of dazzling colour, sparkling and glittering, rolling into place in the mosaic.

"Where have these come from?" I asked, still unsteady on my feet.

"These are the treasures of darkness that attached themselves to you in there," the Potter explained. "You thought the enemy was pelting them at you, but they rained on you from heaven's storehouses, and now they add sunshine to your path." I looked up and saw the sun beaming on these trophies of suffering, and indeed the path was growing brighter and brighter.[31]

It was then that I noticed that the path led to another door, and there on the mat stood my muddy boots.

---

[30] Micah 7:8
[31] Proverbs 4:18

10

Baca

The label on this door was "Baca"[32]. I knew the meaning of this Hebrew word, and it was not encouraging.

"Uh-oh," I groaned.

"Yes, this is your weeping room," the Potter said compassionately. "Your grief room. You go in there alone with your Friend, but you are not permitted to record your experiences. No one truly knows your grief except your Creator, your Everlasting Father, and it is not for anyone else to hear. You are invited to express your deepest sorrows with all your heart, and" – he gave me a knowing look – "this is the room to wear your boots!"

As I pushed my heavy feet into the boots, they fit, but so uncomfortably! I trudged through the doorway, dreading the release of the tears of all the years. There are no words to describe the pain or the tender lovingkindness in that room. I would not have been able to record it even if it had been permitted. I may have been in there a week, a month, a year, until eventually my Friend led me through an outside door where the Potter greeted me with a cool cloth and refreshing

---

[32] Psalm 84:6

drink. He asked no questions. He led me beside the still waters, he let me lie down in green pastures; my soul was restored.[33] Eventually my swollen eyes could focus again, and it was then that I noticed the enormousness of the place.

---

[33] Psalm 23:2

11

A Broad and Rich Place

I had come through such soul-storms and now here I was in a broad and rich place.[34] There were delights of every kind. Somehow, incomprehensibly, in this house of houses I could walk in the forest; I could wonder yet again at the fragile harbingers of spring; I could splash on the beach; I could listen to waves; I could look down from mountain tops; I could rest, rest, rest; I could feast on my favourite foods – sweeter and more tantalising than my senses had ever known. It slowly dawned on me that I was enjoying these pleasures with my Friend alone – and Garry not there! I had wondered whether the memories of those shared pursuits would ever lose their bitter winter taste, but here I was welcoming the budding spring greenness without him. Panic-stricken, I found the Potter and tugged his sleeve.

"Am I forgetting him? Should I feel guilty? Dare I find pleasure again without him?"

He gestured to my hands. I was holding my bowl of Garry's precious love to my heart, as always, but I noticed it seemed bigger, heavier – though not *heavy*.

---

[34] Psalm 66:12

The Potter explained, "You will notice that your kintsugi bowl is floating in a larger bowl."

It was. I hadn't noticed.

"This bowl contains water from the springs of the valley of Baca, mingled with your tears; the perfect cocktail given for you to comfort others as you have been comforted.[35] Love received and love given are the perfect partners to heal the wounded soul, softening the harsh brush-strokes of your experience in the Mirrors of Time. Always remember, though, that no one truly knows another's sorrow except their Creator, their Everlasting Father. You are but a broker of His perfect comfort."

Something happened in me at that moment. Something eternal, transcendent. The griefs of my life began to make a tiny bit of sense. Through a glass, darkly,[36] I began to see that loss could be gain. In the Eucharist room, my Prince had talked of the joy set before Him in His sufferings, and the thought brushed me ever so lightly that someone could be comforted through my own sorrows, with His comfort. The concept brought me joy, but at a level far deeper and higher than earthly happiness. I could not recapture it when I relied on my own understanding. I would have to let it take its course.

"Come," the Potter said, "let's walk and talk."

"This was my favourite thing of all with Garry," I said.

"I know," he said. And we walked and talked.

---

[35] 2 Corinthians 1:4
[36] 1 Corinthians 13:12

It was all so peaceful and calming until... the noise of traffic, all manner of traffic. I looked around to see its source and it was then that I noticed the door marked "Goodbye".

12

The Goodbye Room

There were vehicles everywhere! Aeroplanes, buses, taxis, motorbikes, helicopters, all coming and going from different stations and airports. There were platforms (but no seats, I noticed), lost property offices, safe deposit boxes – and noise, noise, noise! People were hurrying around, being directed by very friendly and helpful staff. They seemed to be leaving their luggage in lockers, or disposing of them down a huge chute, and then being provided with new cases and bags, or they climbed into vehicles empty-handed. Some were waving goodbye; others were being introduced to each other; and a few were completely alone, as I was, *as I am*. All of them were wearing headphones.

The Potter waited until I was more accustomed to the fast pace of this place, then commented, "This is not a destination, you know. People are passing through, saying goodbye to release them to say hello. It's an opportunity to listen to fresh direction, to let go of unnecessary clutter and to be refuelled for the next leg of the journey. You see that some of them are leaving relationships behind and connecting with new companions."

"Surely they need to rest before moving on," I said. "Why are there no seats?"

"They have all spent time in the broad place, as you have," he explained. "They are ready now, as you are. But first, look up."

A plane was taking off above my head and everyone was watching it leave. On the side there was an image of an enormous albatross and, in huge letters, the slogan "Let go and let God".

"My mum used to say that," I observed.

"Indeed," he replied. "There have been many powerful influences in your life. All have contributed to your mosaic. But" – and here he leaned towards me with that 'listen up, I am going to say something you'll want to remember' look – "you do not have to let them control you. The 'Let Go and Let God' plane takes away anything and everything that is no longer appropriate for your current reality."

I had a moment of realisation! "The albatrosses around our necks!" I exclaimed.

"Exactly! Well done!" he said. "But remember, it doesn't just say 'let go'; there's the grace to go with it: 'let God'. There is always the grace to go with your Father's advice."

"Then why is it so difficult to do what He says?" I really wanted to know.

"Oh," he chuckled (he often chuckled about my questions, as though he knew the answer was easier than I thought), "it's not difficult to do what He says. *Not* doing what He says is what's difficult!"

I thought about this for some time. It was true. When we know the right thing to do and don't do it, we have a terrible time. It haunts our waking and sleeping hours, as we try to justify our procrastination.

The Potter picked up my thoughts, of course. "And then you do what you know to do and your soul is at rest. Compliance is easier, because you are programmed to live as your Father created you to."

"Like admitting when we're wrong..." I offered.

"...is easier than self-justification."

"Or saying sorry..."

"...is easier than minimising the hurt caused."

"Or forgiving..."

"...is easier than nursing a grudge."

We ping-ponged the ideas back and forth until he finished with, "And there is always more than enough grace."[37]

I heard a bell ringing close by. It was then that I noticed a bus pulling up next to us, with the initials V.V. on the front.

---

[37] Romans 5:20

13

I Meet the Prince of Peace Again

The Potter ushered me on to the vehicle, but I realised I was no longer holding my bowls. Distraught, I begged him to let me find them. How could I be so careless with my precious Garry's precious love?

"Hush!" he said, with his hand on my shoulder. Once again, I was completely calmed by his words and actions. "The bowls are in a locker, safe and sound. His love and the comfort of Baca are part of you now, absorbed into your soul. They will always be there."

I had to acknowledge that I was needing external tokens of our love less and less, and the comfort for my tears was becoming more accessible.

I turned my attention to the bus. "What do the initials V.V. stand for?" I asked.

"Welcome aboard the Vindication Vehicle!" he declared with a bow and a smile, as we moved off into a well-lit tunnel. There were huge hoardings either side of the tunnel, and as they came into focus, I saw to my horror that they were plastered with glaring images of the very same fears and failures that had taunted me in the Eucharist room. I was appalled, dismayed. "I thought these had been dealt with at the Cross!" I exclaimed.

"Oh, they were," the Potter reassured me, "but what will you do with the memories, the images? These are but pictures, and yet you are as disgusted with yourself as if they were the real thing!"

"Please tell me, what should I do?" It was true. I was disgusted, distraught.

I followed the Potter's eyes to the front of the vehicle. There sat the Prince of Peace with the table prepared as before. Suddenly, my senses became aware again of those glorious tastes and aromas, and I hurried to sit with Him.

"Come," He invited, "take, eat and drink, but first…"

I looked up, curious, as He removed His outer robe. To my amazement it was replaced immediately with exactly the same garment. As He rose and walked to me, I could hardly breathe. He handed me the robe; it felt weightless, like a tiny baby in a shawl – you know she weighs a few pounds, but it feels as though you're holding less than nothing.

"Put it on," He said, so I did. What else could I do?

"This is your robe of My righteousness[38], and you wear it because of what I have done for you. Your accusers cannot penetrate the spiritual intensity of this reality. Let us eat and drink and celebrate My victory and your freedom. Your vindication comes from me!"[39]

I broke down and sobbed with gratitude. It was as if that robe was made of active bleach, and every stain of my life was completely eradicated. I knew this was how things were

---

[38] Isaiah 61:10
[39] Isaiah 54:17

going to be from now on. Every time I ate the bread and drank the wine, I would remember this – this newness. I thanked Him and thanked Him, and thanked Him again, and then I went back to sit with the Potter. He was wide-eyed with wonder.

"I have seen this a hundred million times and more," he said, "but every time is like the first time. He is truly mighty to save!"

We continued our journey in silence, ignoring the blasphemous hoardings, both of us revelling in the extravagance of the Saviour's sacrifice. I knew the Mirrors of Time would superimpose the reflection of my new robe of His rightness over those grotesque images. My eyelids began to droop, my soul's burden lightened, and I slept for as long as I needed, a rare experience.

When I woke, I heard water; and as I opened my eyes, I gradually made out a carved sign on a huge oak tree: "Healing Streams".

14

The Healing Dilemma

I was ready to bolt. Oh no, I was not ready to explore the healing dilemma. That was a box, a door, that I had closed firmly, and that was how it was going to stay.

"Come," said the Potter, "let's paddle."

For the first time I refused his invitation, would not budge from my seat. The peace of my sleep evaporated in a cloud of misgivings, confusion and desolation. I knew I was pouting, but it was just too difficult, beyond even my compliant nature; I could not find it within myself to cooperate.

He sat down next to me, no reproach.

"What do you think I'm asking you to do?"

"You want me to listen to you telling me why Garry wasn't healed, or rather why he was healed and then he wasn't; how we got it wrong. Or worse, you want to say that he was taken – by God or by the devil, or maybe that he just wanted to go and leave me because the sickness and pain had worn him out."

"How about I just want you to walk through the streams with me?"

"I'm sorry," I said, "I just can't do it. I cannot face the unanswerable questions. I thought they didn't matter, but they do, they matter so much to me."

"Honestly, trust me, I just want to walk with you. We don't have to talk about anything." And then he asked, "Can you wiggle your toe?"

I knew this approach. At other times in my life, when I had to face some mountainous challenge, my Friend would encourage me to wiggle my toe, then my foot, then my leg, until eventually I could rise from the place I had believed I could never leave.

"I can wiggle my toe," I conceded. And I did. I felt the slightest strength of will return in this simple act of obedience. It made me smile, and it made the Potter smile. He had brought obedience within my reach – such grace!

"How about the foot and the left thumb?" He was teasing now and I relaxed. I reached my hand to his and he helped me to my feet. I was still very, very apprehensive, but as always, the surrender was easier than the resistance, and I let him lead me to a healing stream.

For the longest time the Potter did not talk as we paddled in those streams. I remembered that he had said to trust him that we would just walk, so if there was going to be a conversation, I would be the one to break the silence. I had so many thoughts about healing that I didn't know where to start, especially the old (but very real to me) 'chestnut' that some appear to be healed and others not. Deep down, I knew that there are answers to all the seeming inconsistencies, but trying to dismiss them was like burying a balloon in a bowl of water.

"It does feel a bit random, God's healing," I commented, as airily as I could.

"Go on," he said.

I was on thin ice here, because I only half-believed in the arguments I was going to put out there, but half was enough to keep me awake some nights.

"Well, I have prayed for the sick for years, and read countless books with teaching and testimonies, and there doesn't seem to be a pattern."

"But you believe there is one?"

"Yes, I cannot deny that my Everlasting Father is faithful and true and right about this. No amount of disappointment and perplexity will make me believe otherwise."

The Potter's head shot up suddenly. "Can you hear it?" he asked.

"Hear what?"

"Heaven's pleasure! There is such pleasure when heaven hears faith.[40] Your stand on your experience of healing is pure faith, and it pleases your Everlasting Father."

I was ready to move on to my next point, but the Potter hushed me.

"Pause for a moment," he said, "and let that soak in. Absorb heaven's pleasure so that you will recognise it again. You are so used to counterarguments that you almost apologise to yourself and others for this childlike stance, but we want you to relish the favour that heaven pours out on simple faith."[41]

---

[40] Hebrews 11:6
[41] Jeremiah 17:7

I stood still in the stream we had reached, and a fine fragrant mist enveloped me. I breathed it in and somehow felt more sure than ever of God's integrity. Not self-justification, more like a child discovering that the times tables work in a complex maths problem.

After some time, whatever time meant in that place, I ventured to say, "I really don't want to talk about healing any more. Is that okay?"

"Of course," the Potter reassured me. "Let's move on to the next room."

I was so relieved that I could hardly breathe. To think that I was not being forced into concepts that perplexed me was beyond astonishing. The thought came to me, *I do not exercise myself in matters too high for me.*[42]

"Your Friend often does that, doesn't He?" the Potter commented. "He loves to remind you of a Bible verse that corresponds with your thinking."

"It's one of my favourite things about our friendship," I agreed.

"All those chapters and verses you have committed to memory are like a gold reserve in your heart, a bank account, so to speak. There is a current account which you can draw from at any time, and a savings account which will help transform your sufferings to work for you an exceeding and eternal weight of glory.[43] It will fund the good plans we have for you, the future and the hope."

"I am so grateful for the gift of a retentive memory," I offered, but I sort of knew what was coming next.

---

[42] Psalm 131:1
[43] 2 Corinthians 4:17

"Well, there's that," he said, "but your Friend can also prompt you – and anyone – about verses that you haven't memorised."

"That's true. I'm even more grateful for that!"

The Potter continued, "What He also loves is that you set about memorising these new revelations from Scripture. There is a reward for this, you know, in terms of heavenly communion."

I thought of all the times I had lain in bed going through Bible verses I have learned over the years.

"He is very close to you at those times," said the Potter. "And He genuinely is joining you in the A to Z game!"

I was embarrassed now; no one else knows that I play this game with my Friend. We think of Bible verses beginning with the consecutive letters of the alphabet. I used to play that with Garry, and I miss it so very much, so now I have asked my Friend to share with me; I know I'm not alone, especially when new ideas come to mind.

"He wants to be included in everything, you know, not just the seemingly spiritual. Now more than ever it is true that you can sense His immediate Presence, because He has so much more *space*. That's what makes you shine, and that's what makes Him attractive to other people."

I was listening intently, watching the Potter's kindly face, so I was surprised when he suddenly turned and drew me to a halt. It was then that I noticed the tiny, cushioned stool beneath a label that read "Better Thing".

15

The Better Thing

My name was embroidered in golden thread on the cushion, and when I looked closely, my nicknames were also there, any variants that I'd ever known.

"It's awfully small," I observed, "and I'm awfully tall!"

"Try it," the Potter said. "It's the perfect place for you."

I was not convinced. With my long legs, I have always experienced all sorts of trouble lowering myself to such stools and crouching there, let alone getting up again!

"Try it," he repeated gently, offering his hand. "You are never asked to face earth's challenges without heaven's help."

I knew the Potter well enough by now that we would soon start the toe-wiggling process, so I took his hand and descended gingerly until I could feel the cushion. Immediately I gasped, "Oh-h-h-h!" for it was as though I had landed on an ocean of living, bubbling water which held me afloat and kept me steady. The Potter laughed, not teasing but genuinely having harmless fun at my expense. There was nothing spiteful or condescending in his 'I told you so' expression, just affection and joy that I was now so unexpectedly relaxed.

Then he pointed at a Mirror of Time on the wall, and there I was, lowering myself with an expression of such comical apprehension that I laughed with him, comfortably. I knew that this moment would sweeten my bitter memories of thoughtless teasing about my unusual height. Suddenly, the Potter paused, turned and his face lit up as the Presence of the Prince of Peace filled the place.

"We have entered His courts with joy!"[44] he whispered and left the room. Everything in the room was now glowing gold, and I noticed the mosaic floor around me was also made of pure gold.

I was so very, very happy to be with my Prince, so very, very privileged that He would just appear and share time with me. I was even more happy to be sitting at this low place. I knew how Mary of Bethany must have felt in His Presence, since with all my heart I wanted to give Him my most precious possession, something that meant everything to me, something that would express how grateful I was to belong to Him, to sit at His feet. However, I had no alabaster box of precious perfume, of course.[45]

I considered the gold watch that Garry had given me, or my cross and chain, but these were not enough. Nor were mere words. I could say it a thousand times with a thousand tongues, but this needed to be an offering that cost me something, everything. Then I knew; it would be my wedding ring, the symbol of my love for Garry and his for me. The Potter had reminded me in the Kintsugi room of the unparalleled privilege of being loved as I have been, and I had

---

[44] Psalm 100:4
[45] John 12:3

learnt by now that love is one of heaven's most valued commodities, so I took the ring and laid it at His feet.

"Do you love Me more than him?" He asked.

"You know, Lord." Really, I didn't.

"What was his love language with you?"

I knew that. "It was time spent together. Quality time, where I wasn't busy or distracted."

"Then this is what you are giving Me. Quality time, the one thing needful. The better part, better than a hundred years of slavish service."

In this moment of bare honesty, I knew I had a confession to make.

"Lord," I said, "this is one of the hardest things for me, to sit quietly and give You my full attention. I'm always thinking of the next thing I want to say, or something I need to do."

"Would you like Me to make it easier for you?" He offered.

I was surprised by this.

"I thought if I really loved You, it would be easy. As it is, it feels like a duty, a discipline. I'm sorry. I'm so very sorry."

I really was dismayed when I acknowledged this stinginess of mine with the hero of Calvary, and I knew that if there was to be a genuine and lasting change, I would need to accept His offer.

"You are forgiven," He said. "You are completely clean because I say so, with no condemnation."

"Thank you," I replied, relishing the peace these words brought, yet wondering how He was going to address my fickle heart. His next question was a real poser.

"When do you find it easy to concentrate unreservedly?"

I could not think of one time or situation that qualified and said so. "At the moment it's hard to stay focussed on anything," I mused. "Is it part of the grieving?"

"Oh yes," He affirmed, "and it won't last. But here's what we'll do..." He leaned towards me, and I was agog with anticipation. "I will give you dreams!" He proclaimed with a flourish of His hand. "When you wake up, your Friend will remind you, and you can write them down. All you have to do is this: as you go to sleep, thank Me for the coming night's 'show'!"

This was wonderful! I couldn't wait for nightfall.

As I left that room a long while later, I reflected on the extraordinary truth that the sacrifice of my ring had actually been no sacrifice at all in the context of His loving Presence. I had received far more than I had given.

There was a note from the Potter on the next door. It said simply, "Sweet dreams!"

16

Dreams

The room was generously furnished with everything I needed for a good sleep, so I rushed to settle down, silently thanking my Prince and looking forward to the night's 'show'. Sure enough, I had four dreams, and sure enough, my Friend helped me to remember snippets of them. In fact, there were images on the wall that clarified the memories!

The first picture was of an encounter with a highly respected minister known to my church. I was waving my hand for some reason, and he looked both surprised and shocked when he saw it.

The second picture was about buying a jumper and choosing a colour. I decided against blue and settled for cream.

The third situation was unclear; I just had a sense of satisfaction that everything was working out.

The fourth was a large light-coloured lorry in the distance coming round a corner towards me from the left.

As I looked at the images, I thought about my friends who love interpreting dreams. They would have their notebooks at the ready to hear what the Potter had to say! First, though, he had a question:

"What would you usually be doing now about the dreams?"

I have read a number of books about dreams and gathered a few strategies. I wasn't sure whether they were going to be useful here, but I told him the ones I generally used.

"I would be thinking about my feelings, words and actions in the dreams, any thoughts or events that might have triggered the content, and people represented by the characters, including aspects of my own personality and emotions."

"Shall we do it?" he asked, with an expression of such anticipation that I couldn't resist him. With my nod, he said excitedly, "We'll do it your way, and I'll add anything you want. However, the important thing to remember is to focus only on the snippets your Friend has brought to your mind, otherwise it becomes more academic than spiritual."

This was new to me, as I have always tried to dredge my memory for the rest of a dream, even attempting to go back to sleep to pick up where I left off. Now I could see that I could just let my Friend speak to me about what mattered at that moment – the gold and silver and jewels, as it were. Here was yet another occasion for peeling down to the precious; it was happening a lot in this house, and proving so restful, if somewhat humbling. I was beginning to see that humility is far less demanding than trying to prove myself.

The Potter was growing restless. Clearly, he was as excited about the meaning of the dreams as I was.

"Number one," he announced, flourishing his arm at the first picture, "the waving hand."

I thought I'd guessed this one. "I wondered if he was looking at my nails, which were looking even. This minister knew I used to nibble them until my Father helped me to stop."

"Well, that's marvellous indeed" – the Potter was genuinely thrilled that the Father had done this work in me – "but it's not what the dream meant."

Oh well.

"He was looking at your ring finger."

Of course!

"He was surprised and shocked that you had removed it, wasn't he? The dream reflects how you are processing the immensely significant act in the Better Thing room. The minister represents your most spiritual self, the part of you that you respect as having good judgment based on a spiritual understanding of the Word. The application of the dream is to continue to reflect on this new relationship with your Prince. Equally important is to act on it! Expect Him to love and cherish you and be your hero as your Husband."[46]

He was silent for some time while I absorbed this revelation, my ever-ready tears flowing freely, dripping through my hands. They soaked into the mosaic, especially those ugly black ones, and transformed them into silver nuggets. When I was ready to move on, he refused.

"The application is to reflect, so reflect," he advised.

Two thoughts came to mind: one was the time – recently – when I couldn't open a jar of sauce, however much I

---

[46] Isaiah 54:5

strained to turn the lid. This was a job for Garry, Garry my strong man – but Garry is no longer with me, so at the time I wondered if I should just go without the sauce. Without thinking, I prayed, "Lord, help me," and tried again. Honestly, the lid just twisted off easily, and I marvelled that this was my reality now, even day-to-day practical help from my Prince.

"Truly, the Lord is the strength of your life!"[47] the Potter interjected.

The other thought was about an email, supposedly from my energy provider, offering me a rebate. I just felt uneasy about it and did not respond. Previously, I would have asked Garry (well, actually, he would have dealt with the utility bills!), but Garry is gone, so I checked it out myself and, sure enough, it was a scam. Again, I was so grateful that my Friend had nudged me, taking the husbandly responsibility for my security and for our finances.

And now another thought, this time from the Bible story about Ruth and Boaz. I recalled how, in response to his kindness and the prompting of Naomi, Ruth approaches Boaz and in effect asks him to take her on with all her needs, all her baggage.[48]

The Potter knew what I was pondering, of course, and commented, "That's what He wants, you know, for you to ask Him – and expect Him – to take you on. He will protect, cherish and provide for you in ways you cannot imagine."

"I'd like that," I said simply.

And equally simply he replied, "Then it is done."

---

[47] Psalm 27:1
[48] Ruth 3:9

We sat in silence as I drank this in, and I cried some more.

Eventually, he helped me up and drew me to picture number two, the jumper.

"Why did you choose the cream over the blue, Lizzie?" he asked.

"I really don't know," I replied. "It was a soft blue that I like, and both colours suit me."

"So the dream is about choices," he explained. "Not all choices are black and white, good and bad. You have such a relationship with your Friend that you just wouldn't choose the unsuitable, so you're left with only the likely options. When you arrived at this house, you mentioned the 'blank horizon' and 'unfamiliar context'..."

"You remembered!" I exclaimed.

"Word for word," the Potter agreed. "Every word, every tear, every sigh. You are never alone, never unheard, never unnoticed."

He continued, "The horizon is blank only to your eyes, the context unfamiliar only in your estimation. We know exactly what is coming round the corner."

"Like the lorry dream!" I was really caught up in this now.

"Yes, indeed, but don't forget the third dream, the sense of satisfaction that everything is working out. Use your Spirit-given imagination to picture the lorry off-screen at the depot, being loaded with all things necessary from the riches of the Father's glory.[49] That is where everything is being worked out to His satisfaction, even good processed from

---

[49] Philippians 4:19

evil, curses turned to blessings.[50] You would be amazed at what arrives at the depot to be transformed."

"Like the broken and soiled pots," I commented. "What a place this is for restoration!"

"Seen and unseen," he murmured.

I had a question, but I wasn't sure it was allowed.

"Surely you also remember what I said when you arrived!" The Potter was clearly incredulous as he read my thoughts. "You can ask anything!"

"Oh, of course, yes." At the time, I had felt so ashamed of my questions that I thought I would never dare to air them. Even now I was trying to answer them myself before asking, so that I could use appropriate words.

"You know, Lizzie, permission to ask any questions includes the wording. Remember, the Father says He will answer you and show you great and mighty things that you do not know,[51] so there is nothing to be gained by second-guessing!"

Of course, he knew! I don't know how many times I was acknowledging this awareness of being understood, that I was bringing nothing new to the table prepared for me. I felt as though I was moving into the known rather than the unknown, like a hand slipping slowly into a glove and finding it was tailor-made, completely suited to require-ments.

"Well, I'm just wondering whether you could give me a hint about what's in the lorry." There, it was out!

---

[50] Nehemiah 13:2
[51] Jeremiah 33:3

He smiled. "You told me from the start that you don't like not knowing what's coming, but we love you for learning to take one step at a time. Can you think of it like a sculpture, that every step is chipping and shaping you for your future?"

"But how far off is my future," I wailed, "and what does it entail?"

The Potter touched my arm. He was oh, so gentle!

"Lizzie, the very next minute is your future, and then it is your past! You are in your future now. Do you see?"

"This is heaven's joke again about the word 'now', isn't it?" I queried.

"It is," he admitted, suppressing a chuckle.

"I still don't really get it," I grumbled quietly.

"You will," he said loudly, and then he clapped his hands. "Now, you were thinking about a tailor-made glove, were you not?"

"You know it," I said, smiling again. It would take a real effort to stay grumpy in that environment of love and acceptance.

"Then let us proceed to the next room. We call it the Glove Compartment." Of course, he thought this was hysterically funny, and I loved his unabashed amusement at heaven's humour.

17

The Glove Compartment

The room was gloriously bright because sunshine poured through the magnificently framed windows. It was filled with enormous golden chests inscribed in minute lettering, thousands and thousands of names, like rolls of honour.

"Each chest contains a particular type of glove," the Potter explained, "and the names are of those who have worn them."

I never ceased to be staggered by such detailed knowledge and recording of our lives on earth.

"This first chest contains the gauntlet gloves, worn by those who have risen to the challenge of warfare and overcome the enemy of their souls. He reached through the side of the chest – how did he do that? – and pulled out three gloves of different sizes.

"Blood stains!" I exclaimed in horror.

"Oh yes, some have resisted to the point of shedding blood,"[52] he said, "and their reward is great. The Father values highly the blood of His children, and it does not go unavenged, though these precious warriors may not see it in

---

[52] Hebrews 12:4

their earthly lives. Even now, as I speak, there are those who are suffering unspeakably for their love for their Father, one family in particular." He dropped to his knees and wept and wept. Suddenly, he looked up at me and beamed.

"It is well," he smiled. "The saints are praying and the hosts have been dispatched."

I made a mental note to include the suffering church in my prayers, now that I had experienced heaven's response to the suffering and to the prayers.

"Your Friend will remind you," the Potter reassured me, perceiving my fear that I would forget.

"There is so much to pray about," I sighed. "I know I don't pray enough."

"You know, Lizzie," he replied, "it is not how much you pray, but where you are directing your prayers. Does the psalmist not say, 'In the morning I will direct my prayer to You, and I will look up'?"[53] The quantity of your prayers and confessions is more than enough, but you don't always believe in them because you are directing them any-old-where as you go about your daily life. Even brief arrow-prayers in the midst of business are effective and powerful, when you aim them straight!"

And that, right there, hit the mark! That was why my prayer-life was so unsatisfactory. I was not connecting with heaven.

"But tell me, what can I do?" I pleaded. This was so important to me. How many times had I berated myself for distractions and wayward thoughts?

---

[53] Psalm 5:3

"Here is a simple strategy," he said gently, so encouraging, with no condemnation. "Just take a breath before you pray, or whenever you notice yourself becoming distracted. Imagine one of your special times with your Prince in this place and direct your words to Him. But before you speak, smile at Him. The smile is one of the best connectors in heaven and earth. Your Friend will help, as always."

Of course! Take a breath and smile! Isn't that recommended on earth for launching communication, whether intimate or for the business presentation? I knew it would help in my heavenly communications, so just for practice and for fun, I took a breath, looked up at the Potter and smiled.

He reciprocated and we laughed. We laughed in disproportionate measure to the context, but I knew that all the burdens and shame of my inadequate prayer experience were being laughed away. I sank to the floor (magenta pink had now been included in the mosaic) and breathed such grateful thanks. *A Mirror of Time nearby was decorated with a beatific smile.*

"So, let's look at the names," the Potter urged.

Curious, I stood up and followed him, expecting to see the names of mighty saints and warriors from Bible times to the present. They were there of course, but to my amazement, the Potter drew my attention to my own name!

"When have I ever worn such gloves?" I gasped.

"Your divorce," he replied carefully. "Many times, Satan desired to have you and sift you,[54] but we prayed for you,

---

[54] Luke 22:31

and you rose to the challenge and overcame. You did not give in."

I had never told anyone of this temptation, but heaven had recorded it, of course.

"Then, throughout Garry's sickness and death, the temptation to adjust your theology to your experience was strong, but heaven fought alongside you, and you stood true to the faithfulness of the Father's character, and the integrity of His Word. This is not forgotten in the Mirrors of Time."

At last I could admit the excruciating dilemma I faced, as a leader, of public disappointment in the area of healing prayer which I still completely believed in. I knew better than to side with the accuser of God's people[55] and blame who-knows-who, so I just settled for admitting ignorance and a willingness to learn what I do not yet know.

The Potter interrupted my thoughts with, "Your vindication comes from Him,"[56] and we moved on.

As we approached the brightest and smallest of the chests, he opened it to release the sweetest fragrance, almost reminiscent of the Eucharist room, so I was not surprised when he whispered reverently, "These are called Heaven's Gloves, worn by those who have touched the Father's Presence so intimately that they hardly dared move." The gloves were almost transparent, gossamer-light, reflecting the window's sunshine like mother-of-pearl.

I was honoured to find my name on the chest, and I remembered with hushed gratitude those rare, precious moments. We did not talk of them. We did not dare.

---

[55] Revelation 12:10
[56] Isaiah 54:17

The next box was gold but plain, if gold can be plain, but on the lid sat a huge trophy inscribed with the words "First and exalted".

"What does this mean?" I asked.

The Potter quoted, "'The last shall be first'[57] and 'he who humbles himself shall be exalted'[58]. These are the menial gloves, made of rubber and plastic, soiled, torn and worn, used by those who did what their hands found to do, the tasks refused by others, the work that no-one noticed unless it wasn't done."

I was surprised that this chest did not sport the longest list of names.

"That is because," he answered before I asked – again! – "the roll is only for those who do their work 'unto the Lord and not unto men'[59]. Like all service, the menial jobs can be carried out in self-interest."

I knew just what he meant, so I did not expect my name to be on the roll. We did not look and that spoke for itself. I felt sorry, though not condemned, and I determined to ask my Friend for help.

"He will," the Potter said softly.

The next chest was shaped like a wheelbarrow, full of gardening gloves, some still attached to what looked like crooks.

"These belong to our shepherds and gardeners, those who tend our flocks and vineyards."

"They all look the same size," I observed.

---

[57] Matthew 20:16
[58] Matthew 23:12
[59] Colossians 3:23

"These labourers wear the gloves on behalf of the Master Gardener, the Chief Shepherd,[60] and they must grow into them until they are like Him. So much is expected of young leaders, but remember they are growing into their role, following the steps of their Lord. Which leads me on to the last chest we're looking at today…"

He slipped his hand through the side and drew out the oddest item I had ever seen. It had fingers, yes, but the palm was large and thick, almost like a builder's kneepad.

"Have you guessed?" he teased.

"More gardening?" I suggested.

"Try again!" He was enjoying this.

"Mountaineering? Sports?"

He shook his head, then in a stage whisper he prompted, "Knees. Knees!"

The penny dropped.

"Prayer!" I exclaimed in triumph.

"Prayer gloves are best worn on the knees," he remarked, "even if it is only the posture of the heart."

Then he showed me a scroll, and I noticed it was one of several, hooked around the sides of the chest. Names and names and names!

He smiled at my wonderment.

"Oh, we accept all manner of prayer and supplication in His Name," he pronounced with satisfaction. "Any age, any stage, any language – human or divine, any need, any number, bold or tentative. It's the Name, you see. You do see, don't you?" he added, anxiously.

---

[60] 1 Peter 5:4

I knew better than to miss this opportunity, so I gestured for him to continue.

"He is the Door of the sheep,[61] the crucified One who tore open the veil. His Name gains you entrance to the Throne Room. His Name deflects all accusations of disqualification, for He still bears His wounds of victory as the risen Saviour."

This was like being served with a massive steak when I was expecting beans. It would take a while to digest the welcome truth that there is no disqualification for those who trust His Name.

Eventually, though, I noticed a noise – a happy, busy noise; the unmistakable sound of children playing.

"Come through to the nursery," the Potter invited. "You will love it in here."

---

[61] John 10:9

18

Room for the Children

As we entered, the children rushed over and clamoured to be close to the Potter. He knelt and hugged them all, handing out goodies from his apparently bottomless pockets. I noticed the children passing them round with no snatching, grabbing or stockpiling.

"They know there is more than enough for them all," the Potter explained, "so there is no need for selfishness."

I nodded as I thanked the tots who were sharing with me.

"And that," he continued, "is lesson number one in this room."

The children took our hands and drew us to their play corner, where a large circle of teddies sat, wearing cardboard crowns decorated with shiny jewels. Their paws were raised towards a chair in the middle. The bigger boys and girls were making a stand for a splendid rainbow they had all coloured, and they placed it over the chair. The younger ones were creating a huge figure from yellow blocks. They enlisted the Potter's help to place it on the chair, and someone drew a beaming smile on the top block. Yellow streamers were pasted to the figure, and all the children threw sticky golden glitter over it. They then sat behind the teddies and sang praises to their Saviour and Friend. Every now and again, someone would shout, "Hallelujah!" and they would all push their teddies face-down to the floor, crowns falling before the figure, the children laughing with all their might.

"This is their favourite game," the Potter whispered to me. "No-one taught them, but they have seen it so often in the Throne Room,[62] which they tell me is their favourite place, that they wanted to reproduce it here."

"Who teaches them those sweet songs?" I asked.

"Oh, they just make them up as they go along, rhymes and all! Sometimes the angels come in and sing along, and of course the most exciting moments are with the Prince Himself."

At the mention of His Name, the children's faces lit up and they sang some more. It was such a happy place.

"Lesson number two," the Potter said, "worship is a happy thing!"

Some time later, the door opened and an adult brought in a jug of milk, placed it on a low table and called, "The milk of the Word!"[63]

The children immediately stopped whatever they were doing and raced to the table, found their cups and drank thirstily.

"How is that the Word?" I enquired.

"Watch what happens next," came the reply.

As each child finished his or her milk, they blew through their straws and a cloud of words burst out in bubbles and

---

[62] Revelation 4:10
[63] 1 Peter 2:2

floated around the room, releasing the exquisite scent I was beginning to recognise from the Throne Room. The children dashed about, bursting bubbles and shouting the words, forming sentences and phrases. Spontaneously, they composed a simple song with actions, and within minutes, all knew the verse off by heart, clearly eager to include us as they turned our way.

I will never forget that verse, "Desire the pure milk of the Word."

"And that," laughed the Potter, "is your final lesson in this room."

As we headed for the next door, I noticed a picture under the word "Choices".

19

Decisions, Decisions

The picture was of a mountainside with two tunnels running through the left-hand side. The tunnel on the left was completely impassable, with boulders, rocks and rubble before its entrance.

I was puzzled. "Surely there is no choice if one option is closed off?"

The Potter was expecting this; he nodded and smiled.

"Both were once open, but the rocks and boulders represent the arguments that contributed to the decision."

I could make sense of this. "I think I understand. Faced with two choices, I amass this heap of boulders, and gradually they will be stacked more on one side than the other; then, when I have made my best decision, I move all of them to clear the way I've chosen."

"And is there a problem with this approach?" he asked gently.

"Oh, definitely," I admitted, "because sometimes the boulders can apply to both sides, and I'm left with two half-open tunnels."

"What would usually fuel your final decision?"

"Time pressure, impatience, people pressure, personal preference, fatigue and resignation would force a premature decision; and I hope common sense, research into the facts and a conversation with my Friend over the Word would inform the better ones, but even so..."

"Would you like some tips?" he offered.

Of course I would, I thought.

"Of course you would!" he put in for me, then continued, "We know you would not knowingly make ridiculous, rebellious decisions, directly opposing the Father's Word. We know that you generally listen to your Friend, so here are a few new thoughts."

I wished I had a notebook or my phone to jot these down.

"Your Friend will remind you!" he whispered.

"Of course, I keep forgetting," I said, and we both giggled.

"First of all, remember the Word advises you to acknowledge Him in all your ways,[64] so picture yourself taking the first choice with Him right in it, then do the same with the second. Set Him before you always, and you won't be moved in the wrong direction.[65]"

I could do that. I love a picture.

"I know you do," he smiled.

He had done it again!

"Second, see yourself waking up on the first morning of your life with the first choice. Will you be glad you made that choice of job, church, house move, relationship or conversation? How will you feel about living with that choice? Do

---

[64] Proverbs 3:6
[65] Psalm 16:8

it with all your choices and talk through your feelings with your Friend."

I liked that idea also. "My husband used to say that today's decisions, words and actions are like seeds we sow for the harvest we walk through in the future," I recalled.

"This is true," the Potter agreed, "but don't forget grace. Remember that your Mirrors of Time could also be called Mirrors of Grace. Your Father can intervene and turn things to good,[66] even your bad choices, if you'll turn with Him and let Him. His grace abounds to those who turn to Him, and the inevitable can be softened."

I knew I could list a thousand times my Father had done this for me, undeserving.

"And they are all forgiven and remembered no more!"[67] he reassured me.

"This knowledge is too wonderful for me!" I sighed. "The love and acceptance in this place, the nearness of His Presence, the truthful clarity of His Word. I want to stay here forever making the best choices!"

"And that right there is your third tip!" he exclaimed. "When you set your affections on things above, all the boulders will roll of themselves!"

No, I didn't get it.

"Some would call it seeking first this Kingdom[68] – the righteousness, peace and joy in the Holy Spirit[69] that you are experiencing here. Ask yourself, will my decision bring me and other people closer to the King, the source of all the truly

---

[66] Romans 8:28
[67] Isaiah 43:25
[68] Matthew 6:33
[69] Romans 14:17

best things? How can I best bring heaven to earth in this situation? The boulders that don't contribute to this quest will move over to the other side."

I knew my Friend would love this course of action; I could feel Him bubbling with excitement. The Potter sensed it too, and we spent a few moments revelling in His Presence.

When I looked up, I noticed an up-and-over door which led to a garage.

20

Amber Light

In the garage stood an old-fashioned sports car, old and grey, with its engine running. The most striking feature was the headlights either side of the engine, which were switched on and both amber in colour.

"That's an unusual colour for headlights," I commented.

"This is called the Amber room," the Potter replied, "and it gives further clues about guidance. So much to learn from the colour amber!"

"I suppose it means to get ready?" I ventured.

"Yes," he replied, "but get ready for what? Get ready to stop or get ready to go?"

"Could it be both?" I asked.

"Exactly!" he smiled. "Every word of guidance requires a willingness and a preparation to stop something and to start something in some measure."

I pondered this, then remembered, "I have heard it called the entering-leaving crisis."

He nodded. "That is why the amber light is your friend. We do not rush your readiness, we give you time to process the whole sequence, with all the help you need from your

Friend the Holy Spirit. Chat them over with Him, all the options and how you feel about them."

"Isn't there a risk that I just dither along in indecision?" I asked. I realised that this was a particular risk now that I had no Garry to chivvy me.

"Well, you can dither along in this old sports car for a little while until you reach the green light. Remember, you have a new Husband now who will help you with that final step of decision-making. Trust Him in new ways, expand your expectations!"

"What happens at the green light?" I dared to ask, somewhat cheekily, and of course the Potter saw through me.

"No specifics," he grinned, "but trust me, that old sports car still has plenty of power and potential – a bit like you!"

Now who's being cheeky? I thought.

"Me," he replied.

"Actually," I said, "that is the best news I've heard all day – if we have days here?"

The Potter guffawed. "You're getting it!" he laughed. "*Why* is it the best news you've heard though?"

"You said that I still have plenty of power and potential. That is such a relief at my age and stage, and alone. I feel as though at retirement I was at my peak, and then we went to Asia and came back unexpectedly because of the pandemic, so our master plan kind of fizzled out. I'm still ready to take on something new, as I was with Garry."

"Absolutely," he agreed. "We have great plans for you, a future and a hope, with an expected end, as we did for Garry. But remember, you are in the amber vehicle, dithering through the entering-leaving process. Don't rush yourself, because we do not want to abort the mission!"

"Oh dear, "I sighed. "You know me so well!"

"We know you and love you, and we are acquainted with all your ways,[70] and we've accommodated them skilfully in your future. All you are invited to do is to acknowledge Him in all your ways, and He will direct your paths."

"I remember when you accommodated my dithering in the pink jumper episode," I chuckled.

"Oh yes, when your Friend gave you a word of knowledge at that big meeting..."

"And I asked who it was for..."

"And He said they would be wearing a pink jumper..."

"And I was so nervous, not to mention baffled, when I couldn't find a single woman with a pink jumper in all that crowd!"

"And then came the fun! We were loving it from here!"

"A young man in a trendy pink jumper! I dithered and dithered while the people in the long prayer line were going across the stage. Eventually I plucked up courage and went to him and told him the word of knowledge. He broke into tears and said that as I spoke those words, his father had reached the front of the prayer line and was being prayed for."

"The word of knowledge related directly to the situation with his father. Wasn't it brilliant, Lizzie?"

"Yes, the timing was perfect, and I had nothing to do with it!"

"So will you trust heaven, Lizzie, in the future, as you step out in obedience, that we will take care of the context?"

"Now that I have remembered that episode, I will."

---

[70] Psalm 139:3

"Your Friend will bring all things to your remembrance," he reassured me. So kind! "Oh, and one more word about guidance..." he added. "The Mirrors of Time will show you that you were always *drawn* by your Friend and not *driven*. This is another clear way of knowing who is at the helm."

I heard a few more stones slipping into the mosaic floor and shuffling the colours into a new pattern.

Suddenly, the Potter announced, "Now for something different. A Bible study."

I looked up in surprise and saw that we had reached a door labelled "Isaiah 54. Great Expectations".

21

A Bible Study

"This is the place," the Potter explained, "where you can learn more about what to expect from your heavenly Husband. This chapter can apply to His church, His people Israel and to every individual believer."

I looked around for a screen, anticipating an online teaching session.

"I know you prefer a hard copy," he winked. "Read it aloud as you love to do and let's listen to what your Friend has to say through the Word."

He produced a large scroll with beautifully ornate but legible lettering, and I read it through a couple of times. In this quiet place with no distractions, it was easy to recognise my Friend's voice. I nudged myself to remember to come aside to such quiet spots more often.

"He will remind you," the Potter said again. This was becoming a refrain!

Always go with your first thought, face-value; what does it say? As I made lists under each heading that came to my spirit, I knew my family would be chuckling. I often quote a friend who says that a list makes a molehill out of a mountain when faced with a busy schedule. I found it to be the same in this study; simply writing down what the verses said about husbands, wives, children, foundations, protection and more, gave a memorable overview of the chapter. I was loving it.

"And now look up," the Potter urged excitedly. "See what has happened!"

I looked up and there He was: my Prince of Peace!

"I have come," He said with such tenderness, "to reveal Myself in My Word."

Here I was again, breathless with wonder.

"Let's make a list," He smiled, "about what this chapter tells you about Me."

I could hardly peel my eyes from His face, but as I scanned the verses, I spoke out each name, each phrase about who He is and what He does. My voice was hushed, reverent. This was worship, to be telling Him face-to-face what is eternally true of Him, to be agreeing with this written Word. (How could I not agree when He was standing before me? All 'buts' and 'what abouts' lay at His feet.)

"Thank you," He said quietly, and I knew He was enjoying this deep communion.

I repeated some of the phrases with words of thanks because I knew it would make Him happy, and I wanted that more than anything in this holy place.

After a few minutes, He took my hand and drew me towards the far wall. "Behold!" He exclaimed, laughing now. "A screen!"

I laughed too. I was enjoying being myself and being teased affectionately, like in our family gatherings at home.

"Did you notice that thought?" my Saviour asked. "You are enjoying being yourself. It's because you are loved here for who you are. We formed you perfectly, you know, for the life We planned for you," He said with a smile.

"Thank you," I responded. I had never enjoyed being myself in quite this way before, ever.

"And now you are ready to enjoy this. The screen is here to show what the passage tells you about *you*," He explained. "As I speak, the pictures are created, and you will see how heaven is working in your life to fulfil Our Word."

I was warming to the idea of the screen.

"Remember these images," He said, "in your daily journal pictures. They are like the dreams we have promised, and as always, our Friend..."

"...will remind me," I finished for Him with a grin.

"Here we go. Hold tight!" He warned.

Well, the screen burst to life as my Prince spoke out words and phrases from the chapter. There were scenes from my past and present, some of which I recognised, but others were completely different from my own take on them. I wished I had known then what I was seeing now, in those moving Mirrors of Time.

"Remember," He confided, "this is how your Father designed these scenes, so always ask our Friend to show you heaven's perspective, just as you see in the Mirrors of Time."

"This would have saved me a lot of disappointment, perplexity and frustration," I commented.

"Mm-hmm," He agreed.

I realised that I was learning a new way of Bible study, a conversation with its author!

"You can do this with what you call your 'confessions'," Jesus said. "Address Me personally as you speak out your words of faith and it will multiply your confidence immensely."

Now I was really excited! I imagined saying, "My God shall supply all my need according to His riches in glory by Christ Jesus,"[71] as though speaking to Him directly, as I was here.

"You also found this to be true, didn't you, Lizzie," He commented, "when you accidentally included Garry in your faith confessions after he came here?"

"Yes, I realised that all my faith confessions are entirely true of him there with You. He is indeed completely healed and whole in body, soul and spirit. He definitely dwells in the secret place of the Most High."

"And no weapon formed against him is prospering!"[72] He added.

"And he is seated with You in the heavenly places."[73] I was warming to this, and my Friend was prompting me thick and fast. I sensed He was in His element, and so was I.

We exchanged these biblical affirmations for some time, and I found my faith expanding like a mind-map, taking me to places previously untouched by my prayers, let alone a confident expectation of something good.

Eventually He said, "You know, this is equally true for you before you shuffle off your mortal coil. Remember this 'now faith' which the Potter has tried to explain to you. My Word has no beginning and no end; your faith in the now-

---

[71] Philippians 4:19
[72] Isaiah 54:17
[73] Ephesians 2:6

ness of it is the evidence of things not seen on earth, the substance of things hoped for[74] – but these things are seen here, eternal realities. Garry sees them, and not through a glass, darkly. Garry knows as he is known.[75] He too is in his element."

I was so happy for my Garry. I was perhaps the only one who knew the yearnings of his heart, what he had hoped his 'element' would be and how desperately he had tried to attain it in this life.

"And now his joy is full in My Presence. He is who he always wanted to be, and at my right hand he has all the pleasures[76] he ever wanted!" The Saviour's radiant expression was unspeakable; I sensed He was alluding to the joy set before Him at the cross, and I was beyond grateful. Suddenly, He reached out His hand and lifted my chin so that I would look and listen.

"Lizzie," He said, so gently, "Garry is also in his prime. You have found it so difficult to forget his poor body at the end, but now, receive My Word: *he is in his prime*. Find the best photo you have and imagine the image improved a million times, and you will have the merest beginning of an inkling of how well and hearty and robust he is now. Meditate on this thought until it eclipses the bitter memories and I will make them sweet."

So, I did. I meditated on this and all the other recent revelations with joy and wonder. I would have stayed there for ever, but He said, "This room and every room here is to fuel you for the journey ahead. Your every experience with

---

[74] Hebrews 11:1
[75] 1 Corinthians 13:12
[76] Psalm 16:11

Me is to be enjoyed to the full, but not as an end in itself. It is to bless you for the next step of your walk with Me, drawing closer to Me all the time. This is what I want for you all."

Then casually, as though it were not the most momentous event of my life so far, He said, "Now, let Me wash your feet before you go."

And He did. I cannot describe it.

Then He disappeared and the Potter reappeared from... somewhere. (I had not noticed his departure, so taken up was I with my Saviour.) He had to take me by the hand to the next door, for I was still reeling.

22

The Eye of the Needle

This door was labelled "The Eye of the Needle"[77], and I was puzzled because it was just an ordinary door, not small and difficult as I understood the Bible reference to mean when it mentions the challenges of entering God's Kingdom.

The Potter gestured to the floor, and just in front of the door I spotted a mushroom, a plain mushroom. This did not enlighten me until he said, "Let's look more closely."

So I knelt down and, peering at this small thing, I could just make out a tiny door in the stalk, and on the door a picture of a needle.

"Let's go through," the Potter invited.

Extraordinarily, I assented with no hesitation. I was learning not to apply earth's restrictions to heaven's realities. I have always yearned to experience the 'impossibles' as promised in Scripture,[78] so I was ready to go! As a child, I had easily believed the woodland stories of life below ground, with Annie Ant visiting Enid Earwig in her acorn-cup home, eating crumbs and drinking dewdrops; I

---

[77] Matthew 19:24
[78] Luke 18:27

remembered the Prince's words that we enter the Kingdom as little children.[79]

I felt nothing, no 'shrinking' sensation, as we made our way through this eye, although I surmised that we must be functioning at a microscopic level. There was movement everywhere, and I recognised atoms, molecules, DNA, RNA and such-like from my science teaching days. In class, we had watched and wondered at videos of this activity at a $1:1,000,000$ magnification, and now here I was, walking through its corridors. It was truly beautiful, peaceful, ordered in all things and secure.

"All this is going on in you human beings all the time," the Potter explained. "You have always loved the thought that your Father is working behind the scenes, thwarting the enemy's plans and bringing about an outcome that is beyond the imagination."

I have preached this often. It is one of the most faith-building messages I know, encouraging people not to lean on their own understanding of their situations, but to trust God's unseen workings.

"This image is a brilliant illustration," I breathed. "The evidence of things not seen, things that are visible created from things that are not visible!"[80]

"To the naked eye at least," he agreed, "but that's not all. Your Father also creates from nothing, literally nothing – except His Word, of course. Quantum physicists are slightly unravelling this phenomenon even as we speak. So do not exercise yourself about what you cannot see, or what

---

[79] Matthew 18:3
[80] Hebrews 11:3

seems humanly impossible, for it is there, in the Father's eye!"

"The Father's eye," I repeated, loving the feel of the words rolling around in my thoughts as I remembered those eyes in the Eucharist room and on the Vindication Vehicle.

"You are in there," he assured me, "the apple of His eye[81] – with all His creation."

Those science videos of spectacular magnification had expanded my concept of God's capacity, and I was grateful for this cameo opportunity to revisit a subject I had not enjoyed at school.

"Mirrors of Time," the Potter said with a grin.

"Indeed," I agreed. "It seems that all my encounters in this house are adjusting my reflections from the past."

"Oh yes!" he affirmed vehemently. "We want you to move on into your promised future without the heavy clutter of distorted memories."

This was a blessed prospect, and much more conceivable in the light of this revelation of my Father's intricate involvement in all things visible and invisible.

"And speaking of moving on," he added, "look up!"

And just like that, we were back to normal, looking at another full-sized door – well, not *exactly* a door, more an entrance to a cave, blocked by a huge stone.

---

[81] Zechariah 2:8

23

Mirrors of Time

This was strange: some sort of giant pencil was positioned against the stone as a kind of lever, ready to roll it away from the entrance. There was a pink notebook and pen hanging on a spur of rock next to the giant pencil.

"What happens here?" I asked, genuinely mystified.

"Here I leave you with your Friend," the Potter replied, a tinge of wistfulness in his voice. "You write with Him the chronicles of Lizzie, and then... well, then He will tell you the next step."

He hugged me, spoke the priestly blessing over me,[82] and then he was gone. For a moment I felt alone, as I had felt in the hospital room when Garry was gone, but now I could overlay the picture of my Friend kneeling with me, and my Saviour's tender eyes upon me. As then, the Comforter's sweet Presence took me up and propelled me into a sense of future and hope, impossible to describe. Those who have been in such a room will know what I mean.

I lifted the pen and notepad, apparently activating the pencil to move the stone, to reveal a glass-lined chamber of

---

[82] Numbers 6:24-26

dazzling brightness. Prisms of inexpressible glory reflected from a sun I could not see on to the mosaic floor. The mosaic was... well, *complete*, nothing missing, nothing broken and actually nothing startling; just... complete. On the right were the desk and chair from my den at home, exactly as I had left them. In this light, I could see that the notebook in my hand was my everyday journal, and the pen was one of the many I use from Garry's office.

And there, surrounded by the Mirrors of Time, I wrote this book.

THE END...

Epilogue

...or at least, I *thought* it was the end.

However, as I closed the book and put down my pen, there was a knock at the door, and when I opened it, there stood the Potter. Next to him was a character who reminded me of a man I know who simply exudes fun and humour. Both men's lips were twitching, and they had the appearance of friends who are trying not to look at each other in case they set themselves off laughing. We've all been there.

They were standing this end of a short bridge leading to a tall door at the other end. Well, I say *leading*, but it actually stopped short of the door by a few feet, with something like white fluffy clouds spanning the gap.

"Come to the Laughter room with us," squeaked the Potter's friend, gesturing to the bridge. His shoulders were set like a man nearly suffocating with suppressed mirth.

"Yes, your Friend would like you to visit this one last room before you leave," the Potter affirmed, clearly pleased with himself for managing a coherent sentence without giggling.

Well, who could refuse that invitation, impossible though it appeared?

As we approached the door, I noticed that it had a large reflective window, quite high up, and some writing which I could not yet make out.

We stopped where the bridge ended, and I asked, innocently, "How are we going to get across?"

That did it! The men could contain themselves no longer and laughed helplessly for some time, while I stood sullen, a victim of 'The Bug'. This is the term we used in my youth to describe the phenomenon of feeling excluded from a shared hilarious joke or exciting spiritual experience, while everyone else is having a riotous time. We've all been there.

They scanned my face for signs that I was including myself in their fun, but there were none. Eventually the Potter's friend gasped, "The window!" and pointed in the direction of the top of the door. I noticed that this was more of a one-way mirror, and as I looked up I caught the reflection of an irritable-looking tall woman flanked by two buffoons staggering around on the edge of the bridge.

I was still not amused.

At last, my Friend the Holy Spirit came to my aid, as He always does.

"Lizzie, how have you ever entered into a spiritual moment?" He asked as gently as ever.

I was in no mood to even think cooperatively.

Undeterred, of course, He prompted, "You start where you are. Every journey begins with one foot where you are. When you received your Saviour, you asked with your human voice and the everlasting miracle took place. When you received Me, the Holy Spirit, you asked with your human voice and here I still am, your best Friend forever. When you prayed in tongues, you started with your human voice and I gave you the words.[83] When you feel unwilling to obey, you wiggle your human toe and I give you the grace. It

---

[83] Acts 2:4

is the same with taking the medicine of a merry heart[84]– if you will begin, I will carry you."

I was uncertain, so many questions and doubts.

"Isn't it wrong for me to be merry after my personal tragedy?"

"It is not."

"Won't the troughs of sadness seem deeper after the peaks of merriment?"

"It will be worth it, and the trend will creep upward, so that the troughs will actually become less deep."

"Will people not misunderstand a joyful expression?"

"This is your journey, Lizzie, not theirs. Those who love you will be delighted."

It was then that I noticed that with every question we were moving between the end of the bridge and the door. The Potter and the other man were moving – well, reeling – with me! Like Peter on the water,[85] I looked down at the nothingness under (and over) my feet and panicked, but my Friend the Holy Spirit urged, "Laugh! Laugh with all your might!"

"How can I laugh in all this sadness?" I screamed. And then the laughing lyrics of an old, familiar children's song came to me (from my dear, faithful Friend, I know): "Ha, ha, ha, ha, ha, ha, ha, ha, ha, ha, ha, ha." So I sang it. I considered that I was at risk of dying now, so I may as well die laughing in this place of hope.

"Louder!" the three chorused.

---

[84] Proverbs 17:22
[85] Matthew 14:30

"HA, HA, HA, HA, HA, HA, HA, HA, HA, HA, HA, HA!" I bellowed, and the three swelled the song, one of them unbelievably out of tune.

Now this was funny! Three people and an invisible Spirit laughing, singing at the tops of their voices to the tune (or almost to the tune) of a children's song, floating in the middle of nowhere... or somewhere.

I sensed it bubbling up. I felt my lips twitch. I heard the tiniest chuckle deep, deep down. The two men held their breath, the Spirit breathed on my tiny chuckle, and through the door we went.

As with the Baca room, experiences in the Laughter room cannot be expressed in words. I'm reminded of another Bible proverb: "Each heart knows its own bitterness and no one else can share its joy."[86] Sufficient to say that I left that room equipped for the next leg of my journey, with new strength,[87] with the oil of joy, with a new garment[88] – and a smile!

---

[86] Proverbs 14:10
[87] Nehemiah 8:10
[88] Isaiah 61:3

About the Author

Lizzie Hunt is a retired speech and language therapist, international missionary and Christian speaker. She was inspired to write this book following the sudden passing of her husband, Garry, in 2021.

With a passion for allegory, personal development and her Christian faith, she hopes her writing can provide others experiencing their own grief with the comfort and healing she felt while writing it.

Lizzie has two adult children – Julia, who lives in Asia with her husband and two children; and Jonathan, who is married and lives locally.

To contact the author, please write to:

Lizzie Hunt
c/o Onwards and Upwards Publishers
4 The Old Smithy
Rockbeare
EX5 2EA

Similar Books from the Publisher

The Ascent
Peter Grant
ISBN 978-1-911086-90-1

Peter Grant tells a story in which Jesus invites him to climb a mountain together. "Something stirred deep within me – a longing to be closer to God, to spend more time with him, to get back on track." At each stage of their journey upwards, as they encounter new places and people, Peter receives fresh wisdom and revelation, as his relationship with Jesus ever deepens.

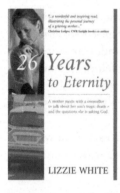

26 Years to Eternity
Elizabeth White
ISBN 978-1-78815-627-1

When a young Christian teacher, active and well-loved in his community, was killed during a traffic accident, his mother Lizzie found herself struggling to make sense of all that had happened, particularly from a faith perspective. In a series of discussions with a fictional counsellor, Lizzie tells her true story, sharing memories of her son that will make you laugh and cry, but also tackling head-on issues of suffering, loss, forgiveness and hope. As we sit in on these counselling sessions, we join Lizzie on her journey of asking questions and deepening our understanding of God, of life and of eternity.

Books available from all good bookshops and the publisher's website:
www.onwardsandupwards.org